The name of this book is

Billy's Neighbors

The authors are Alta McIntire

Wilhelmina Hill

The artists are Janet LaSalle
Lucy Ozone

The book was made for you by **Follett Publishing Company**
of Chicago, Illinois

Look here for the
names of the stories
in this book

Vacation

4

Was Fun

5

SIGHTSEEING

UNIT I

My Picture Dictionary

an airplane

Maplewood

beach

Miss Dale

Billy's neighbors

on a slide

6

draw

park

found a surprise

picnic

game

read stories

in a swing

summer vacation

Happy Days

"I am happy to see you,"
said Miss Dale.

"Did you have good vacations?"

"My vacation was fun," said Ann.

"I went to the zoo.

It was fun to see the elephants eat.

And I liked to see the monkeys play.

I liked the farm animals, too.

They are in the children's zoo."

"Going to the zoo is fun," said Billy.

"A farm is fun, too.

I went to my grandmother's farm."

"What did you do on the farm?"
asked David.

"Grandmother let me help with
the work," said Billy.

"She let me get the eggs.

I helped feed the animals.

I helped to milk a cow.

It was fun to see all the animals."

8

9

"I played at the beach," said Alice.

"We made houses and a store of sand.

Mother said they looked like a little city.

We looked for things in the sand."

"What did you find?" asked Tom.

"We found a surprise," said Alice.

"It was a big turtle.

We went home and read Billy's book
about turtles."

"I went to the library," said May.

"The librarian read good stories to us."

Bob said, "Barbara and I worked.

We helped in my father's store."

"We had picnics in the park, too,"
said Barbara.

"We like to eat in the park.

We played on the swings and slides.

And we played games.

It was good fun."

Picnic in the Park

Come let's go on a pic-nic in the park,

Stay all day from ten o'-clock till dark;

Base-ball, skat-ing and man-y things to see!

11

Pack a lunch for we'll be hun-gry as can be.

From: MUSIC ROUND THE TOWN, *Follett Publishing Company, 1955*

Pictures Tell Stories

All the children wanted to tell
their vacation stories.

Miss Dale asked, "Would you like
to draw pictures?

You can make your pictures tell stories.
They can tell your vacation stories."

"Yes," said the children.

"That will be fun."

"I will have a surprise
in my picture," said Bob.

"I have a surprise, too," said David.

"How pretty they look," said Ann.

"It is fun to read the stories
they tell," said Tom.

"I can read Barbara's story,"
said Alice.

"I see David's surprise," said May.

"Billy's farm picture is good,"
said Bob.

"They are all good," said Miss Dale.

"I can read all the stories they tell."

13

This is how the pictures looked in the room.
Can you read the stories they tell?

Which vacation would you like?
Why would you like it?

What did you do in summer?
Can you tell the story in pictures?

Miss Dale's Vacation

"It's your turn, Miss Dale,"
said the children.

"Did you have a good vacation?"

"I had fun, too," said Miss Dale.

"I liked my airplane ride best.

This poem will tell you why I liked it."

The children liked the poem.

Miss Dale helped them read it.

Can you read the poem?

In An Airplane[*]

Girl: When I'm in an airplane,
                 I see the world below.

Children: Rivers, lakes, and endless plains,
                 And mountains, row on row.

Boy: When I'm in an airplane,
                 Riding through the sky,

Children: I feel how big is the whole
                 wide world,

Child: How very small am I.

From: MUSIC ROUND THE TOWN, *Follett Publishing Company, 1955* [*]

Maplewood Friends

The children you read about in this book live in Maplewood.

They go to the Maplewood School.

Friends in Maplewood helped the children have good vacations.

They help to keep the children well.

They help to put out fires.

They help many people.

They are good neighbors.

The stories in this book are about Billy's neighbors.

Who are your neighbors?

Tell something a neighbor did for you.

Tell something you did for a neighbor.

Why do you like to have good neighbors?

Firemen Are Good Neighbors

19

UNIT 2

My Picture Dictionary

bed

long ladder

birds

matches

fire boat

motor

20

fire engine

pipe

fireman

pole

firemen's clothes

safety signs

CHILDREN CROSSING

FIRE ESCAPE

hoses

water hydrant

Firemen Help Animals

"A big fire engine was at my house this morning," said May.

"Oh! Did you have a fire?" asked David.

"No, the firemen came to help my cat. She was up in a tree. She would not come down."

"Did they get her down?" Tom asked.

"Yes," said May. "A fireman went up for her. He went up on a ladder. She was happy to be down. She did not like it in the tree."

"What did the fireman say?" asked the children.

"They said that they help many kinds of animals," said May.

"How can they help birds?" asked
Alice.

"My friend has a bird," said Ann.
"It lives in her house. One day she
could not find it. She looked and looked
in the house. It was not there.

"A fireman came to help her. He
looked in a tree and there it was! My
friend was happy to have her bird again."

22

"I have pictures that tell how
firemen have helped animals," said Miss
Dale. "You may see the pictures. Can you
read the stories they tell?"

The Fire Engine Goes to School

"Maplewood firemen like to tell Maplewood children about their work," said Miss Dale. "They come to the schools on a big fire engine. They will be at our school this morning."

The children and Miss Dale went out to see the engine.

"We have come to tell you about our engine," said a fireman. "We want you to know about fires. We want you to be careful with fire."

"What a long engine," said Billy. "And how long the ladders are!"

"Yes, we take this engine to fires in big buildings. We go up the ladders to help people and to put out the fires.

"Sometimes people come down the ladders. Sometimes we have to help them down."

"Look at all the hoses," said David. "There are big hoses and little hoses."

"Yes, we have big hoses for the
big fires and little hoses for the
little fires," said Mr. Bob, a fireman.

"We take the hoses up the ladders,"
the fireman went on. "Then we can turn
water on the fire."

"Where do you get the water?"
asked Barbara.

"We have water for the little fires
in the engine," the fireman said. "We
get water for big fires from a water
hydrant.

"A water hydrant is like a big pipe. There are hydrants on the streets in Maplewood," said the fireman. "Do you know what they look like?"

"Yes," said the children. "Sometimes in summer a fireman or a policeman turns the water on. It runs into the street from the hydrant. We like to play in it."

"Do you like to be firemen?" asked Alice.

"Yes, we like to help people," said Mr. Bob. "We like to put out little fires. We do not want little fires to be big fires."

"We will sing our new song for the firemen," said Miss Dale.

Where's the Fire?

Rhythmically

Ding! Ding! Ding! Ding! Hear the cry,

See the trucks rush - ing by,

All the peo - ple run and shout,

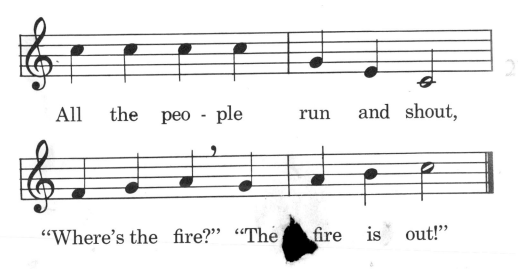

"Where's the fire?" "The fire is out!"

From: MUSIC ROUND THE TOWN, *Follett Publishing Company, 1955*

"We like the song," said the firemen.

"Thank you and good-by."

And away they went on the big engine.

What Will Burn?

One day Mr. Bob came to school again. This is what he said to the children.

Mr. Bob: Look at what I have, boys and girls. Who can find something that will burn?

Billy: The book will burn and so will the paper bag.

Ann: The little house and the tree will burn.

Alice: The airplane will burn.

Mr. Bob: What do you see that will not burn?

David: Sand will not burn.

Barbara: Water will not burn.

Tom: You can't burn the bell.

Bob: The money will not burn.

Mr. Bob: What do you know about fire and clothes? Do clothes burn?

28

Billy: Yes, clothes will burn. We
        should be careful and not go
        too near fire.

Ann: We should be careful at picnics.
        Sometimes a picnic fire burns
        clothes and people.

Barbara: Our family likes picnics.
          We are careful about fire.
          We cook and then we put out the fire.

Bob: Yes, we put water or sand
        on the fire to put it out.

Alice: We keep matches put away at
        our house. We do not want
        Baby to find matches.

Mr. Bob: Good! Babies should not have
          matches. Big boys and girls
          should not play with matches.

Miss Dale: Mr. Bob would like to see a fire drill, children. We will see how well we can do it.

Mr. Bob: That was a good fire drill. You will know what to do if you are in a fire.

Billy: We go where Miss Dale tells us to go. She does not want us near the school if there is a fire in it.

Mr. Bob: Firemen can't work well with people near. You can help if you tell little children what you know about how to help us.

The Fire Station

Mr. Bob asked Miss Dale and the
children to come to the fire station.
He told all about the station and how
the firemen live in it.

"This is one of our homes," he said.
"We live in the station a day and a
night. Then we go home for a day and
a night."

"Do you like that?" asked David.

"We get so we like it." said Mr.
Bob. "We like our work, and we have
so many things to do."

"Where do you sleep?" asked Tom.

"We sleep upstairs," said the
fireman. "We will go up there."

They went into a big, clean room
with many beds in it.

"A fireman puts his clothes near
his bed at night. If there is a fire
in the night, he gets into his clothes
and slides down this pole. Then he
rides away to the fire on a fire engine."

"How do the men know where to go?"
asked Billy.

"The people who let us know about the
fires tell us where they are," said Mr. Bob.
"Will all you children find out how to tell
us if you see a fire?"

"Yes," said all the children.

"This is where we cook," said
Mr. Bob. "The firemen are pretty good
cooks. And how we do like to eat!

"We eat in this room. Sometimes
we read and work here, too. Did you
know that we go to school? We have
school work to do.

"We like to go to school. We want
to learn to be the best firemen we can. We
want to learn new ways to put out fires.

"In some cities fire boats put out
fires. We learn about them, too.

"We keep the engines clean and ready
to go. We work on the hoses and the
ladders. When the bell rings, we are
all ready.

34

"Who would like to go up on this
fire engine?" asked Mr. Bob.

"We all would," said the children.

What fun they had! They had turns
on the engine, and Mr. Bob let them ring
the bell.

Then Miss Dale said, "Come, children,
we have to go to school again. Thank you,
Mr. Bob."

"Thank you," said all the children.

"Come again and good-by," said Mr. Bob.

Fires of Long Ago

Long ago people did not have fire engines. They did not have hoses to carry water for them. When a house was on fire, they had to get water from a well and carry it to the fire.

All the neighbors helped. They all worked together to put out fires.

People were careful with fire. They wanted to stop all fires. They did not want any big ones. They could put out little fires, but they could not put out big ones.

35

Then a fire engine was made.
This one was a little engine. Men had
to pull it to a fire.

The firemen did not live in the
fire station. They did not go to
school to learn how to be firemen.
They had other work to do. But when
the fire bell rang, they stopped their
work. Away they ran to the engine house
to get their little fire engine. Then they
would pull it to the fire.

The firemen worked together to help
their friends and neighbors. They did
not like fires. They did not want
their homes to burn.

Then big engines were made.
They were so big that the firemen could
not pull them. Horses had to pull
them to the fires.

Fire horses were big and strong.
They were pretty horses, too. The
firemen liked to feed them well and
to keep them clean.

The men could ride to a fire on
this engine. It did not take long to
get there. They could put out many
fires with the new engines.

Today fire engines have big motors
in them. You know how fast they can go.
It does not take long to get to fires
with the engines of today.

Can You Do This?

1. Write good rules about safety
   with fire. Write rules about:
   (1) Safety at home
   (2) Safety at school
   (3) Safety with matches
   (4) Safety at picnics
   (5) Safety at fire drills

2. Cut paper like bells. Put
   it together to make a little book.
   Write rules about safety with
   fire in your book.

38

3. Make some big signs and write
   safety rules on them. Put them
   up in your school for all the
   children to see.

4. Draw a picture story about
   firemen and their work. Ask
   the others to read the story
   your picture tells.

Good Halloween Fun

UNIT 3

My Picture Dictionary

black cat

library

card

paper bag

40 **cut eyes**

parade

funny face

pet

game

jack-o-lantern

poster

Getting Ready for Halloween

"Halloween will be here soon," said
Miss Dale. "It is a day for good fun.
What would you like to do on Halloween?"

"A parade is fun," said Billy. "May
we have a Halloween parade? We can find
funny clothes, and we can make funny
Halloween faces."

All the other children said they
would like a parade. They all wanted
to wear funny clothes.

"Then look for Halloween clothes
at home," Miss Dale said. "We can make
funny Halloween faces at school."

"Would you like to make Halloween faces like this one?" asked Miss Dale. "Here are some paper bags. You can draw animal faces or faces of people on them."

Everyone made a funny face on his paper bag. They cut out the eyes so they could see.

"We will surprise our friends," said Barbara. "They will not know who we are."

"May the other children in school be in the parade?" asked Alice.

"Yes," said Miss Dale. "I am glad you want to ask them. We can sing a Halloween song for them. We can learn it today."

42

On Halloween

Gob - lins, al - ley cats, witch - es on brooms,

43

Wind in the trees sing-ing scar - y tunes,

These are the things that are heard and seen,

In the dark of night, on Hal - low - een.

From: MUSIC ROUND THE TOWN, *Follett Publishing Company, 1955*

Halloween Posters

The children wanted to make some
Halloween posters. They made pictures
of cats and jack-o-lanterns on some of them.

Ann's poster said, "Do good on Halloween."

"Good fun for everyone," is what
Alice had on her poster.

44

Billy put this on his poster:
"Think of others on Halloween."

"I want to write a poem," said
Barbara. Bob said that he would help
her. They made a poster together.
They made some good pictures. Then
they put this on their big poster:

"The best day of all
Comes in the fall.
Jack-o-lanterns are seen
For it's Halloween."

The children put up some of the posters at school. They took some to the Maplewood Library and some to the stores.

The librarian put the posters up in the library. The people in the stores put them where everyone could see them. The Maplewood people all said, "What good posters!"

Bob's father said, "This is a good way to have fun on Halloween."

The Parade

When Halloween came, the children looked so funny. The mothers came to school to see the parade.

Miss Dale was the leader. They went up and down the playground so the mothers could see them. Then they went all the way to the stores.

The people in the stores came out to see the funny parade. They said, "This is fun for us, too."

When the children went back to school, the mothers had a good surprise for them. They had little Halloween cakes for all.

The children sang a song for
their mothers. Then they all played
a "guess-who" game. Can you play it?

I am a black pet.

I like boys and girls.

You see me on Halloween.

Guess who I am.

I am a big bird.

I live in the country.

I sing "Whoo-oo" on Halloween.

Guess who I am.

Halloween Fun

It is fun to do these things.

1. Make a Jack-o-lantern.
2. Make some good Halloween pictures and posters.
3. Make Halloween cards.
4. Have a Halloween parade. Make Halloween faces and clothes.
5. Tell about safety in a Halloween parade.
6. Make little Halloween books to surprise your friends.
7. Write Halloween "guess-who" stories. Play the "guess-who" game with your friends.

Library Friends

49

UNIT 4

My Picture Dictionary

artist

Miss Brown

author

Mrs. Summer

50   book cover

David   Alice
Billy   Ann

names

hospital

president

interesting book

steps

library card

wild animals

Miss Brown Visits School

Soon after Halloween Miss Dale and the children had a visitor. Miss Brown came to tell the children about the Maplewood Library.

She said, "Book Week will soon be here. We have many new books in the library for Book Week. We want you to come to see them.

"You may read these books in the library. You may take them home if you want to. But you must have a library card if you take books away with you. How many of you have library cards?"

Some of the children said they had
library cards. The others said they
wanted cards. They said, "We like to
read. We like to read library books."

"Take one of these cards if you
don't have a library card," Miss Brown
went on. "Ask your mother or your
father to sign it. After it is signed,
bring it to the library. Then we will
give you a library card."

"We will bring them to you," said
Miss Dale. "We want to visit the
library together."

Going to the Library

The children soon had the cards back at school. All of the cards were signed.

"Now we can go to the library," said Miss Dale. "We must be careful on the way. We don't want anyone to get hurt."

"We will be careful," said the children. "And we will be polite, too."

They were soon going up the steps and into the library. Miss Brown met them and said, "I am glad to see you. Come into the children's room."

How pretty the children's room was!
There were red and yellow flowers in
· boxes. Interesting pictures were in
the room. And there were many shelves
with books on them.

"I will tell you something about our
library," said Miss Brown. "Then we will
look at the new books. We have new
animal stories and many other interesting
stories that you will like."

How to Find Books

"In a library," said Miss Brown, "the books that tell about the same things are put together. That is so they will be easy to find.

"Look at this shelf. Here are books about ways to ride. The books about trains and boats and other things to ride in are together. When you want books about ways to ride, you should look here.

"On this shelf are story books. They are books to read for fun. You may learn some interesting things from them, and you will have fun reading them.

"Here are books about animals. Some of them tell about pets, some are about farm animals, and some are about wild animals.

"You can see how easy it is to find books," Miss Brown went on. "Look for the shelf that has the kind of books on it that you want."

The children looked at all the new books. They looked on all of the shelves.

"All of you have library cards," said Miss Brown. "You may each take a book if you want to."

Each of the children found the book he liked best. They took their books and their cards to Miss Brown. She marked the cards and told the children they could take the books home with them.

Authors and Artists

Miss Brown said, "Sit down and we will talk together. We will talk about books.

"People who write books are called authors," she said. "Look on your book for the name of the author. Let's take turns reading the names of the authors on our books.

"Artists are people who draw pictures for books. Sometimes an artist writes books, too. Let's read the names of the artists who made the pictures for our books.

"Do you think you would like to be an author or an artist?" Miss Brown asked.

Miss Dale said, "We make little books now, Miss Brown. We are the authors and the artists. We write stories in some of the books, but some of the children write poems."

Then Miss Brown read a poem to the children. She helped them read it this way:

The Little Turtle

All: There was a little turtle,

Boy: He lived in a box.

Boy: He swam in a puddle.

Girl: He climbed on the rocks.

58 Girl: He snapped at a mosquito.

Boy: He snapped at a flea.

Girl: He snapped at a minnow.

All: And he snapped at me.

Girl: He caught the mosquito.

Boy: He caught the flea.

Girl: He caught the minnow.

All: But he didn't catch me.

From: COLLECTED POEMS *of Vachel Lindsay, Copyright 1925 by the Macmillan Company*

The Children's Library

"What an interesting visit!" said Alice when they were back at school.

"Yes," said Miss Dale. "And Miss Brown was a good helper. What can we do to make our library more interesting?"

The children told many things. Miss Dale wrote them on a big paper. They put the paper up in the room where all could see it. This is how it looked:

Things We Will Do

1. We will make signs that tell about the library.

2. We will make posters about books, authors, and artists

3. We will make pretty paper covers for old books.

"Now we must make cards to put in our books," said Barbara. "We can make them like the cards in the Maplewood Library books."

"Yes, and we must put the books that tell about the same things together," said May. "Then we can find them when we want them."

What fun it was to get the library ready! The girls made some pretty flowers of paper. They put them on some of the shelves.

The boys made signs and posters. Some told about new books. Others told interesting things about the library.

The boys made pictures on some of the posters. Miss Dale liked their good, careful work.

Billy and Bob made a poster about taking care of books. They put it up in the library. They said, "We want everyone who comes to our library to read it."

How We Care for Books

61

We keep them clean.
We put our books away.
We do not write in them.
We keep book marks in them.

Billy and Bob

The children asked Alice to be the
first librarian. They took turns going
to the library for books.

Every day there was a new librarian.
Every day children went to their library
to read. Every day some of them took
books home with them.

Some of the children brought books
from their home libraries to school.
They put the books in the school library
for all to read.

The children liked all of the books.
They took good care of them. They
did not keep them too long.

A Reading Club

One morning Miss Dale asked, "How would you like to have a reading club? Our club could meet every week. We could talk about the books we read."

"That would be fun," said Ann.

Everyone wanted a club. Miss Dale said, "We can have a president. The president will be the leader. Write the name of the girl or boy you want for president on a paper. Put the paper in this box."

Many children wrote Billy's name on the papers. There were so many that Billy was the first president.

Billy is the first president of our reading club.

The club meetings were fun. There were so many interesting things to do.

One day the children all told about the books they were reading. Each one told the name of the author and the name of the artist. Then they each told something interesting about the books they were reading.

At another meeting, the children showed the paper covers they had made for books. David and Alice had some book marks ready to show. Others read "guess-who" stories.

The children sang a song at every
club meeting. This is a song they all
liked.

America the Beautiful

A - mer - i - ca! A - mer - i - ca!

65

God shed His grace on thee,

And crown thy good with broth - er - hood

From sea to shin - ing sea.

From: MUSIC ROUND THE TOWN, *Follett Publishing Company, 1955*

"My friend works in a hospital," said Miss Dale at one of the meetings. "It is a children's hospital. Some of the children there like to read. They do not have many books. Do you think we can help them?"

"I will bring one of my books for them," said Alice.

All the children wanted to bring books.

Miss Dale was happy about that. She said, "Ask your mother if you may bring a book. See that the book you bring is clean. Bring it in a paper or a paper bag."

The children made pretty covers for the books. They made pictures on the covers that sick children would like. Then Miss Dale's friend took the books to the hospital.

The children made a big book to
give to children in another city. They
told all about Maplewood in this book.

Billy made a picture of the Maplewood
School. It was a big picture.

The other children wrote stories about
what they do at school.

Some made pictures of the playground
and wrote stories about the games they
play there.

There were pictures and stories
about ways to ride in Maplewood and
about many other things.

Ann
If I could
live in a book,
I should like
to be Snow
White. The

These are some of the other things
the children did in their book club.
Would you like to do them?

1. They made a book for Miss Brown
   that told about their book club.

2. Each child made a little book
   of his own. In it. he wrote the
   names of all the books he read.

3. The children cut out paper dolls.
   Then they cut paper clothes for
   them. They made the dolls look
   like children in their books.
   They had a parade of story book
   dolls on a shelf in the library.

4. Each child told or wrote a story
   that started this way: "If I
   could live in a book, I should
   like to be -----." Then they
   told why they would like that.

Policeman Tom
and His Friends

UNIT 5

My Picture Dictionary

a mural

police station

bicycle

policewoman

big strong man

Who are you?
Where do you live?

questions

motorcycle

star

parking meter

uniform

Policeman Tom

walk

wheel

A Good Neighbor

Every school day Policeman Tom
is at the corner near the Maplewood
School. Everyone likes Policeman Tom.
He is always ready to help people.

The children like to see Policeman
Tom in his uniform. They like to look
at his star. Best of all, they like to
visit with him on their way to school.
He is always happy and friendly.

One day Miss Dale said, "Policeman Tom is one of our good neighbors. Would you like to ask him to come and tell us about the Maplewood police?"

"Oh, yes," said all the children.

"Let's make some plans first," said Miss Dale. "Then we will ask him to come."

They talked about all the things they wanted to ask Policeman Tom. Each of the children wrote one of the questions on a paper.

Policeman Tom at School

"We are learning all we can about Maplewood," said Miss Dale to Policeman Tom. "We want to learn more about the Maplewood police and their work."

"I will tell you all that I can," said Policeman Tom. "What would you like to know?"

"We each have a question to ask you," said Miss Dale. "Bob, you may ask the first question."

Policeman Tom

Bob

Barbara

Can anyone be a policeman?

No. A policeman must be a big strong
man. And he has to learn many things.

Do policemen go to school?

Yes. All new policemen go to school.
After that, they must go to school
from time to time to learn new things.

Why does a policeman wear a star?

It tells us that he is a policeman.

74

Is a policeman's work hard?

Sometimes it is hard, but it is   Billy
interesting. People like to work hard
if they are interested in their work.

What do policewomen do?

They work with us in many ways. They
wear uniforms and stars, too, so people
will know them. Some policewomen help
school children at corners. Others help
women and children in big cities.

Ann

 Tom

Alice

May

Do all policemen do the same work?

No, some help on streets. Others go
up and down streets to look after homes
and stores. Some stay at the station
to take telephone and radio calls.

When do policemen go to homes?

Miss Dale

Sometimes people in homes need help.
They telephone the station and ask
for help. Sometimes a neighbor calls
and tells us that someone needs help.

75

How do the men in cars know where to go?

There is a radio in each car. The men
at the station can talk to all the men
in cars and tell them where to go. The
men in cars can talk to the station and
to each other, too. This is why we call
our radios three-way radios.

Do many Maplewood policemen work at night?

 Yes, we need many night policemen. At first, policemen didn't work in the daytime at all. They all worked at night. Now, with so many cars on the streets, we are needed day and night.

Are there many accidents in Maplewood?

Too many. People are not always careful. We don't want accidents. We help people so they won't have accidents.

What can we do to help?

 Children should cross streets at corners. They should look up and down the street. At corners where there are policemen, they should do what the policemen tell them to do. If there are lights, they should go when the light is green.

A motorcycle policeman comes to our
store. His motorcycle has three wheels.
He takes the money from the parking
meters near the store.

Many of our men ride motorcycles. Some
motorcycles have three wheels and some
of them have two.

I saw a policeman at a fire. Do policemen
go to all fires?

We go to all big fires. We keep people
and cars out of the way of the firemen.
And we help people who are hurt or sick.
We take them to a hospital.

Some of the children ride bicycles.
Can you give us some rules for
bicycle riders?

Yes, I am glad you asked that. Here
are some good bicycle rules:

1. Be careful not to run into people.

2. Ring your bell to let people know
   you are coming.

3. Put your hand out to tell people
   you are going to turn or stop.

4. Go the way the cars go. Ride on
   the right side of the street.

5. Don't ask anyone to ride with you.
   Only one child rides on a bicycle.

78

"Thank you, Policeman Tom," said Miss Dale. "The bicycle rules will help us, and you have told us many interesting things.

"We have a poem that we would like to read to you."

My Policeman

He is always standing there
At the corner of the square;
He is very big and fine
And his silver buttons shine.

All the carts and taxis do
Everything he tells them to,
And the little errand boys
When they pass him make no noise.

Though I am so very small
I am not afraid at all;
He and I are friends, you see,
And he always smiles at me.

From: THE FAIRY QUEEN *by Rose Fyleman, Copyright 1923 by Doubleday & Company, Inc.*

Interesting Things to Do

Here are things Miss Dale and the children did after Policeman Tom's visit.

1. They wrote a letter to Policeman Tom to thank him for telling them so many interesting things.

2. They made a big book about Maplewood policemen.

3. They each made a little book and wrote in it the rules for safe bicycle riding.

4. They made a mural in their room. The mural showed people in Maplewood doing the right things.

5. On a big paper they wrote the words they had learned. They put the paper up in the room.

6. Miss Dale read two stories to the children that were told by a policeman.

A Big Surprise

Policemen have many surprises
in their work. One night I had a
really big surprise.

A man had called the station that
morning. He said, "We are going on our
vacation. We will be away two weeks.
Will you watch our house for us?"

"Yes, we will do that," I said.
"We like to know when families are away.
Where do you live?"

"At 122 Spring Street," he said.
"My name is Brown."

"All right, Mr. Brown. Have a good
vacation."

That night I saw a light in the house. "Something funny here," I said. "I will see about this."

I went to the house and asked, "Who are you? What are you doing here?"

"I am Mr. Brown," the man said. "I live here."

"You can't be Mr. Brown. Mr. Brown went on his vacation this morning. Why did you come here?"

"I am Mr. Brown. I forgot something and came back for it. Here, look at this paper. It will tell you I really am Mr. Brown."

"After this let us know if you come back," I said.

"I will," said Mr. Brown. "And thank you for watching my house."

Little Lost Boy

One day I was riding in a car with another policeman. A radio call told us that a little boy was lost.

We went to his house and his mother said, "I don't know where Dick can be. He is so little. He is only three."

"Tell us about it," we said.

"Dick was playing with his toys," said his mother. "I was working in another room. When I looked for Dick, I could not find him."

"What does he look like?" we asked.

After we had seen Dick's picture we said, "We will find him. He can't be far away.

"We went to the neighbors. We went
up and down the streets. No one had
seen Dick. So we went back to the house
to look again.

"We saw some steps. When we went up
the steps, what do you think we found?

"Yes, it was Dick. He was fast asleep.

"Dick's mother was so surprised and
happy. She said, 'Thank you for finding
Dick.' We were happy to find him, too."

Policeman Tom Comes Again

One day Policeman Tom came to school again. He came to talk to the children about pets.

He said, "It's good to have pets. They can be fun. But when we do have pets, we must take care of them.

"One day a woman called. She said some people had put a dog out of a car. He ran after the car. The people said, 'Go away! We don't want you!'

"We found the dog and gave him to a family that would take care of him. He has a good home now.

"There are many people who want pets. People who don't want their pets should find homes for them."

Do You Know These Things?

What should David do?

Why does Tom cross the street now?

How does this policewoman help children?

Dick is lost. What should he tell the policeman?

Maplewood Stores

UNIT 6

My Picture Dictionary

bakery

garden seeds

bank

grocery store

bottle of medicine

growing flowers

88

can of food

hammer

check

ice cream

corn

metal dishes

frozen food

suit of clothes

Plans for Visits

One day Miss Dale said, "There are
many kinds of stores in Maplewood. They
sell things we need to buy. Would you
like to know more about them?

"Yes," said all the children. "Who
will tell us about them?"

"Each of us can visit a store,"
said Miss Dale. "Then we can tell the
others about it."

On the chalkboard:

Stores to Visit

Grocery   5 and 10 cent St
Barbara   Alice

90

"I will tell about my father's store," said Barbara.

"Let me go to the 5-and-10-cent store," said Alice.

"My father will take me to a department store," said Billy.

The other children told what stores they would like to visit.
What kinds of stores are in your town?
Tell what you know about these stores.

Barbara's Story

"My father has a grocery store,"
said Barbara. "He sells many kinds
of foods. Some are in cans or boxes
or paper bags. Some come frozen in
paper boxes.

"We keep the frozen foods cold
in big boxes. We keep the milk cold,
too. We put other foods on shelves
or tables.

"Some of the people find their
groceries. Some like to have
Father or his helpers find them.

"Father lets Bob and me help a little in the store. Sometimes we find groceries for people who need help. We help to keep the shelves clean. We put food on the shelves. And Bob makes signs that tell how much the foods cost.

"We have paper bags to put the groceries in. Then people can carry their foods home."

"Who takes the money for them?" asked Billy.

"They give Father the money as they go from the store," said Barbara. "Father is careful to give them the right change."

92

"Where does your father get the
food for the store?" asked David.

"Some foods come from far away,"
said Barbara. "Some others come
from farms near Maplewood.

"Each day many trucks come to
the store. One brings milk and eggs
from farms. One brings cakes and
other foods from a bakery. Other
trucks bring bags and boxes of many
kinds of food."

Can you tell where the foods you like
come from?

"Do people buy meat at your store?"
asked Ann.

"Yes, they can buy many kinds of
meat. Some of it has been cooked and
put into cans. The meat we call cold
meat has been cooked, too. Most of
the meat is to be cooked at home.

"We sell chickens, ducks, turkeys,
and fish, too. Many people buy them."

"These foods are all good for us,"
said Miss Dale. "They help us to be
well and strong."
What meat do you like best?
How many people who work to give us food
can you name?

Learning to Buy Groceries

1. What foods do we buy in cans?
2. What foods come in boxes?
3. Name foods we can buy frozen.
4. What foods need to be cooked?
5. What foods do not need it?
6. What have you helped cook? Tell how you did it.
7. Can you draw pictures of foods from farms?
8. Look at home for boxes and cans that had food in them and bring them to school. You can put them in a play grocery store.
9. Can you help make a play store for your room at school?
10. Tell what you do and say in a grocery store.

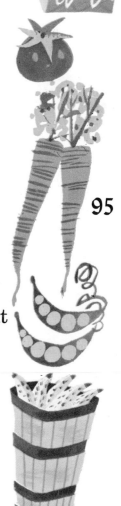

95

The 5-and-10-Cent Store

"I went to the 5-and-10-cent store
with my mother," said Alice. "There are
all kinds of pretty things in it. I saw
many tables and shelves of things to buy.

"I looked at all the things, but
I did not put my hands on them. Mother
told me that people like to buy things
that are clean. They do not want things
that many people have had in their hands.

"I like the toy counter best. I
like the balls and dolls and little cars
and fire engines on it.

"I asked Mother if I could buy a
big ball for the baby. The ball had a little
bell inside. Baby likes to play with it.

"On some counters I saw clothes.
Some had pretty pictures and other
things for homes. There were many
things to help us cook.

"At one counter, people can buy
things to eat. I had milk there."
What have you seen in a 5-and-10-cent store?

"I like the counter where they have pretty flowers. Women and girls buy them to wear.

"I saw all kinds of paper at one counter. There was pretty paper for tables and shelves. There was paper to write on. Mother let me buy some paper to write on at school.

"I had a big surprise when I saw the picture cards. There was a picture of the Maplewood School on one, and the Maplewood Library was on another. There were many birthday cards, too."
Can you find some picture cards of things in your town?

The Drug Store

"I go to the drug store for many things," said Dick. "When Mother was sick, I went there for medicine. It helped her to get well.

"There are many counters and shelves in the drug store. There were boxes and bottles of medicine on all of them. I am glad I don't have to take all of it.

"The drug store sells many things that help us keep clean. It has things to help us look good.

"I like to go to the drug store for something to eat. Best of all, I like the ice cream."

What have you seen in a drug store?

The Flower Store

"I went to the flower store," said
Tom. "I wanted to buy mother a
flower for her birthday.

"I looked at all the flowers. Some
were big and some were little. There
were yellow flowers and red ones. They
were all pretty.

"Some flowers were growing and some
had been cut. I liked a pretty red
flower that was growing. I gave it to
my mother and she liked it, too."
What flowers have you seen growing?
What flowers have you cut?

The Book Store

"I went to the book store to buy a
new book," said May. "I save my money
to buy books. I put it in a little bank.
I call the bank my 'book bank.' When I
have what I need for a book, I buy it.

"Father and Mother buy books at the
book store, too. Then we all sit in the
living room and read.

"I found a book about some children
who went on a visit to a far-away country.
It was fun to read. I will put it in
our library so all of you may read it."

What have you seen in book stores?
What do you read at home?

101

The Pet Store

"I think I went to the best store
of all," said Ann. "It is the pet store.
I saw many kinds of animals.

"The little birds were singing
pretty songs. Some of these birds
were blue, some were yellow, and some
were blue and orange.

"Some of the big birds can talk.
One big bird said, 'Who are you?'

"There were fish and turtles, too.
The woman in the store let me feed
the turtles.

"She takes good care of the animals.
She gives them food and water. She
gives carrots to the rabbits and meat
to the dogs and cats.

"She keeps the boxes where they live
clean. Pets need to be kept clean or
they may be sick.

"This woman tells the people who
buy pets how to care for them. She
tells them what to feed the animals
and how to keep them well."

What pet would you like to buy?

How would you take care of it?

The Hardware Store

"David and I went to visit the
hardware store," said Jane. The man
who runs the store told us why it is
called a hardware store. Many of the
things in the store are made of metal.
Metal is hard. That is why the store
has this name.

"There were all kinds of garden tools
and garden seeds in the store. And
there were hoses to carry water to gardens
when they need it."

"I liked the tools best of all,"
said David. "There were saws
and hammers and other tools.

"There were pans and metal dishes
and other things to cook with on some
of the shelves and tables.

"We liked the toys, too. There were
boxes of tools for children. There were
metal dishes for play in the sand. And
there were bright, new cars and bicycles.
All children would like them."
What metal toys have you seen?
What other things have you seen in
a hardware store?

The Department Store

"My father took me to a department store," said Billy. "He told me all about it.

"A department store is like many little stores in one. The part of the store where they sell food is called the food department. There is a hat department, a book department, a toy department, and many others.

"Father and I went to the department where they had clothes for boys. A man helped us find suits. There were three that we liked.

"We went into a little room. I
put the suits on to see how they looked.
This is the one that was best for me.
I have it on this morning so you can
see how it looks.

"Father asked, 'May I pay for the
suit with a check?'

" 'Yes, we will take your check,'
said the man.

"Father took out his check book.
He wrote what he was to pay for the
suit on a check. Then he wrote his
name. He gave the check to the man.

"The man thanked Father and asked
us to come back when we need another
suit.

"We went to the bank next. Father
wanted to get some money.

"In the bank, Father wrote another
check. A man who works there gave him
money for the check.

"I asked Father if I could write a
check, too. He told me that only people
who have put money in a bank can write
checks.

"The bank takes care of money for
people. When they need money people
write checks. I am going to put the
money I save in a bank. Then, when
I am older, I can write checks."

At the
Little Corner Store

You can   buy some gum and   can - dy,

At   the   lit - tle   cor - ner   store.

109

Su-gar and tea, Nee-dles and thread, Choc-o-late bars,

Cin-na-mon bread; At the   lit - tle cor - ner   store.

From: MUSIC ROUND THE TOWN, *Follett Publishing Company, 1955*

Bob's Story

"My father told me about the first
store in Maplewood. It was not like
the stores that are here now. It had
a little of everything in it.

"People went to this store to buy
food, clothes, tools, and many other
things. It was not big like a department
store. Everything was in one little room.

"Some of the people did not have
money to buy things. So they traded
something they had for something they
wanted from the store.

"Sometimes farmers traded corn, eggs,
or chickens for sugar or pans or tools.
The storekeeper would sell what the farmer
traded to him. He would sell these things
to other people who needed them.

"People liked to go to the store
to visit with their neighbors who were
there."
Did you ever visit with a friend in a store?
What have you traded with other children?

Can You Do These Things?

1. Make a game about stores. Write names of stores on little cards. Write names of things to buy on other little cards. See who can put the right cards together.

2. Make a big chart for each kind of store that you know. Write the name of a store on each chart. Put pictures of things you can buy in the stores on the right charts. Write the money that each thing sells for near it. Now you can play store with the charts.

3. Tell how people at stores have been polite to you.

4. Tell how you have been polite to the workers in stores.

5. Write a little story about how stores help us.

Other Friends Who Help

UNIT 7

My Picture Dictionary

Christmas card

Mr. Park

dairy foods

moving truck

garbage can

postman

Jack

post office

letter

street cleaners

mail

tax money

milkman

yard

A Letter From Jack

One day Mr. Park, the postman, came
to school. He had a letter for Miss Dale
and the children.

"Thank you, Mr. Park," said Miss
Dale. "We like to get letters."

"I like to bring letters," said Mr.
Park. "I have been the postman for
the Maplewood School a long time."

"Will you visit us some day and
tell us about your work?" asked Miss Dale.

"Yes, I like to talk about my work,"
said Mr. Park. "I will come soon."

"When Mr. Park comes again we will have questions ready to ask him," said Miss Dale. "Now, will you read our letter to us, David? It is from Jack."

Dear Miss Dale and Children,

I like my new home on the farm. My Mother and Father like it too.

We have a big house. I have a room with my bed, my radio, and my books in it.

Boots is my pet dog. We run and play together after I come home from school. We have fun.

Will you come to the farm to see us? We want you to see our farm and our pets.

Your friend,
Jack Read

Mr. Park Visits School

One day soon, Mr. Park came again.

"We have questions ready to ask you," said Miss Dale.

"Good," said Mr. Park. "What is your question, Billy?"

Billy: Why do you like to be a postman?

Mr. Park: I like the walk. It helps

to keep me well and strong.

And I like to bring mail that

makes people happy.

Tom: How far do you walk each day?

Mr. Park: About 8 or 10 miles, I think.

Alice: Do you take many cards to people?

Mr. Park: Yes, I take many cards on Christmas and other holidays. People send many birthday cards, too. And people on vacations send many cards.

David: How long do you work each day?

Mr. Park: About 8 hours. Some of my work is in the post office.

May: What do you do there?

Mr. Park: I get my mail ready. All the mail for a house must be together. Then all the mail for a street must be put together in the right way.

Jane:	How many letters do you carry in a day?
Mr. Park:	I really don't know. I take mail to about 300 families.
Alice:	You had a birthday box for me.
Mr. Park:	Yes, I take little boxes. A man takes the big boxes in a truck. I take many papers, too.
Miss Dale:	How can we help you?

Mr. Park:	Everyone can help by writing so we can read it. Some people make e's and i's alike. Others make o's and a's alike. We can't read some of the writing. You can help by watching your dogs, too. Dogs often bite postmen. We like friendly dogs, but we do not like dogs that bite.
All:	Thank you, Mr. Park. We will help.

Other Good Helpers

"My brother, Bill, is a paper boy,"
said Tom. "Some days I help him. We
get the papers ready, then we take
them to people's houses. We keep them
clean, and we put them where people
can find them."

"Moving men are good helpers, too,"
said Jane. "They moved our things in
a truck when we came to Maplewood
to live. They were careful with all of
our things."

"I have a song and some pictures
about other good helpers," said Miss
Dale. "We will learn the song. Then
we will look at the pictures."

The

Gas Station Man

Oh, fill it up, please, Then wash it and grease it,

Please do it as fast as you can!___

We could-n't get far with truck or with car

Were it not for the gas sta-tion man!___

From: MUSIC ROUND THE TOWN, *Follett Publishing Company, 1955*

People Who Help Us Learn

Find people in the pictures who
help us learn.

Name other people who help us learn.
How do they help?

People Who Help Us Go Places

How do these people help us go places?
Tell how other people help.

They Help Us Keep Well

How do these people help us to keep well?

What things can we do to keep well?

They Help Us Have Fun

What do these people do to help
us have fun?

What fun do you like best?

The Milkman

"One day my friend, the milkman,
let me ride on his truck," said Billy.
"Early in the morning, we went to the
city dairy for the milk. There bottles
of milk were put in boxes with ice to
keep them cold. We took milk and cream
and other dairy foods to many homes."

"How many of you drink milk each
day?" asked Miss Dale.

All hands went up.

"Milk is one of our best foods,"
said Miss Dale. "It helps us grow.
We should thank the farmers, the
dairy workers, and the milkmen
for this good food."

"And the cows, too," said Ann.

Garbage Men

"Garbage men come to our house,"
said Bob. "They take the garbage from
a can in our back yard.

"We have a cover for the can. We
put the garbage in paper bags, then
we put the bags in the garbage can.
We want our yard to be clean and pretty,
so we have flowers near the can.

"The men put the garbage in their
truck. Then they take it away. They
get the garbage from many other houses.
They help to keep Maplewood clean."
Why are garbage men good helpers?
How do they help to keep us well?

Street Cleaners

"Street cleaners are good helpers, too," said Ann. "They keep the streets clean and that helps to keep us well. People like to live in a good clean town."

"They help us in winter when there is snow or ice on the streets," said David. What ways of cleaning streets have you seen?

How do street cleaners help to keep us well?

Working for the Town

"Who pays the garbage men and
the street cleaners?" asked Billy.

"The people of Maplewood pay them,"
said Miss Dale. "The people who live
here pay taxes. This means that they
pay money to the town. The people who
have big houses and much money pay
the most. This tax money pays the men
who work for the town.

"Tax money pays the firemen and
the policemen for their work. It pays
for our streets, schools, and library.
It pays for the library books we like
so well."
Does your family help pay the workers
of your town?

129

Can You Tell?

1. Tell about the people who help you and your family.

2. Tell your family what you have learned about family helpers.

3. Tell how you can help little children learn things they need to know.

Can You Do These Things?

1. Draw pictures of workers in your town.

2. Make a picture storybook about helpers.

Farm Friends

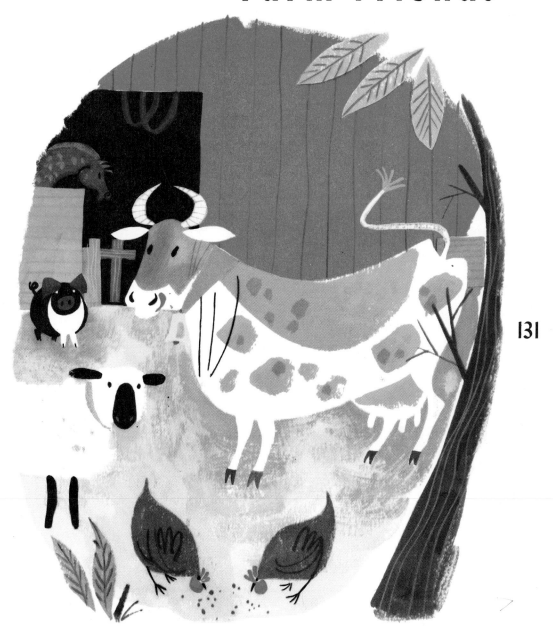

131

UNIT 8

My Picture Dictionary

barn

oats

bus

pigs

calf

plow

132

ears of corn

silo

feed chickens

stall

a good lunch

tractor

mail box

turkey

Going to Jack's House

One day in spring, Miss Dale and the
children went to visit Jack and his family.
They wanted to see Jack's new home and
the farm.

There were many things to see along
the way. Some farmers were at work in
their fields. Cows and horses and other
animals were near the barns.

There was a mail box near each house.
Miss Dale told the children that a postman
brings mail to the farms each day. He
takes the mail they put in the boxes back
to the post office.

The family was happy to see Miss Dale and the children. Mrs. Read said, "Come in. We will visit a little, then you can see the farm."

The Read family asked about all of their friends in Maplewood. Miss Dale and the children wanted to know all about the farm.

Mrs. Read said, "Here is a glass of cold milk for each of you. Our cows give good milk. We drink it every day."

"How good the milk is!" said all the children.

Mr. Read's Farm

"I will take you to see the barn," said Mr. Read. "This is where our cows and horses sleep at night. And it is where we store their food."

"What a big barn!" said Billy. "And what big silos!"

"Yes, I need a big barn and big silos to care for all my animals and their feed," said Mr. Read.

"This is where we milk the cows," he said after they went into the barn. "Each cow has her own stall, and she knows where it is."

"May I go up the ladder?" asked
Billy.

"Yes, if you will be careful,"
said Mr. Read.

"All I can see is hay," Billy
called down. "Hay, hay, everywhere!"

"We store hay up there each summer
to feed the animals in winter," said
Mr. Read. "Hay is dried grass. The
animals like it and it is good for them."

"Come and see what we have here,"
called Jack.

"What a pretty little brown calf,"
said Ann. "What is his name?"

"We call him Brownie," said Jack.
"It's a good name for him."

"What is in that field near the
barn?" asked David.

"That's corn," said Mr. Read.
"We grow corn for the animals. When
the corn plants are big, we cut some
of them. Then we cut up the plants
and put them in the silo. They make
good winter feed that way.

"We don't put all of our corn in
the silo. We let some of it grow as
long as it will. In the fall, we take
the ears of corn from these big plants.
They make good feed for the animals, too.

"We grow sweet corn in our garden,"
said Mr. Read. "Some of our neighbors
grow big fields of it. There is a cannery
near. They take this corn to the cannery.

"We plant oats, too," said Mr. Read.
"Oats make good feed for farm animals."

"How can you do all the work?"
asked Tom.

"I have a tractor to pull my plow.
It pulls other machines, too. It helps
with many kinds of work.

"Would you like a new kind of ride?"
asked Mr. Read.

"We all would," said the children.

"What a good surprise!" they all said.

"This is the best ride I have had,"
said Bob.

Driving
The Tractor

Driv - ing round and round   the field,

139

Here   we   go,   here   we   go,

Driv - ing round   and   round the field,

Up - on   the great big trac - tor.

From: MUSIC ROUND THE TOWN, *Follett Publishing Company, 1955*

Farm Fun

It will be fun to do these things.

1. Find stories about farms in
   other books. Read the stories
   you find to the other children.

2. Make a farm book. You can put
   some of these things in it.
   (1) Pictures that you find at home.
   (2) Pictures that you draw.
   (3) Stories that you write.
   (4) Some "guess-who" stories.

3. Plant some corn or other seeds.
   Put water on them when they need
   it. Look at them every day.

4. Fold a paper and cut farm animals
   that will stand.

Farm Animals

Jack: Come and see our pets.

Tom: I see Boots. And look at her brown and white puppies!

Alice: I like the big brown one.

Jack: Boots likes all of them. She takes good care of them, too.

Mr. Read: The puppies will be good farm dogs like their mother. Boots helps us with the cows and she is a good watch dog.

Jack: Our cat is a good animal for the farm, too. We don't have many mice with her here.

141

Barbara: What noise! What are these animals?

Jack: They are hogs and baby pigs.

Mr. Read: They will give us meat. We get all of our meat from our farm. We have a big freezer to keep our meat in. The meat stays frozen until we are ready to cook it.

142

May: Look at this little calf with her mother.

Mr. Read: The mother is one of our best cows. She gives us more milk than our other cows.

Ann: What do you do with all the milk?

Mr. Read: A milk truck takes it to the dairy. At the dairy, the milk is put into bottles. Then milkmen take it to homes and stores in the city.

The Chickens

Jack: Here come Mother and Miss Dale
to see the chickens.

May: How many chickens do you have?

Mrs. Read: About 500. But 400 of them
are baby chicks.

Alice: Will the little yellow chicks
be white when they are big?

Mrs. Read: Yes, they will be white.
White hens lay many eggs.
I like to keep that kind.

Billy: Is that the chicken house?

Mrs. Read: Yes, we need a big chicken
house for so many chickens.

Tom: They have a big yard to run in.

Jack: Yes, they like it. And they like this corn bread Mother feeds them.

Mrs. Read: You may look in the hen house for eggs.

Bob: Do you get many eggs?

Mrs. Read: Yes, we do. The man from the dairy buys some of them. And we eat as many as we want.

Jack: These hens are sitting on eggs. They will sit there about three weeks. Then baby chicks will come from the eggs.

Barbara: I would like to be here then.

Jack: Come and see the ducks.

Ann: Look at them swim!

Barbara: What funny feet they have!

145

David: Feet like that help them to swim.

Bob: How well the baby ducks swim.

Jack: Yes, they like the water.

Billy: Here comes a big turkey.
What noise he makes!

Alice: I'm afraid of him!

Tom: He won't hurt you.

Mrs. Read: Do you like our farm animals?

Children: Yes, we like all of them.

A Good Lunch

Miss Dale helped Mrs. Read get the lunch ready. They put a table in the yard. They put many kinds of good food on the table. Then they asked the children to come and take what they wanted.

"Get in line," said Miss Dale. "You know how we take turns."

All the children were polite. They put their food on paper dishes. Then they went to sit on the grass to eat.

"This is like a picnic," said Billy. "Do you have many picnics?"

"Oh, no," said Mr. Read. "We have to work hard. We can't have many picnics. But we like the farm. We like to see our crops grow, and we like to care for our animals."

"What do you do in winter?" asked Bob.

"We have work to do then," said Mr. Read. "We feed the animals, and we keep the barn and the chicken house clean. We work on our machines, too. We get them ready for spring work."

"Jack goes to school," said Mrs. Read. "He likes his new school and his new teacher."

SCHOOL B

"Yes, and I like to help on the farm," said Jack.

"Thank you for the good lunch," said Miss Dale and the children. "And thank you for telling us so many things about farms and farming.

"We know a little poem. We will say it for you."

My Father

Boys: My father's a farmer,
　　　　He works all day long,

Girls: His face it is brown,
　　　　And his hands they are strong;

Boys: He plants in the springtime,

Girls: And reaps in the fall,

All: And brings in the harvest
　　　Of food for us all.

From: MUSIC ROUND THE TOWN, *Follett Publishing Company, 1955*

Back to School

When the children were back at school, they did these things. Would you like to do them?

1. They wrote letters to the Read family to thank them for the day on the farm.

2. Each child made a picture to show what he liked best about the farm.

3. They made some pictures of farm foods, and they looked for pictures at home.

4. They told how they had been helped at school, at home, and on the street.

A Time for Telling

150

What Would You Say?

1. What would you tell a little boy or girl
   that you saw playing with matches?

2. What would you tell little children
   about having fun on Halloween?
3. What would you tell someone who
   doesn't know how to get a library card?
4. What would you tell a policeman
   if you were lost?
5. What would you tell little children
   about riding bicycles?

Can You Finish These Stories?

Safety with Fire

Father was burning paper in the back yard.
He told the children _____ .

Fires of Long Ago

Fires of long ago were not easy to put out
because _____ .

Halloween Fun

The best way to have fun on Halloween
is _____ .

My Favorite Book

The best book I have read is _____ .

A Clean Town

Everyone likes a clean town because _____ .

Baby Chickens

Baby chickens come from _____ .

Farm Foods

The farm foods I like best are _____ .

153

Interesting Work

I want to be a _____ because _____ .

Use of Money

We need to know about money because _____ .

Good Friends

The doctor and the dentist are good friends
because _____ .

What Would You Do?

1. What would you do if a policeman told you to go to the corner?
3. What would you do if your ball rolled into the street?
4. What would you do if a new boy or girl came to your school?
6. What would you do if you lost a library book?
7. What would you do if you saw a woman with many bags of groceries?
8. What would you do if you saw a fire in a house?

Where Would You Go?

1. Where would you go to get a good book?

2. Where would you go for a good vacation?

3. Where would you go to buy medicine?

4. Where would you go to buy new clothes?

5. Where would you go to buy tools?

6. Where would you go to have a good time?

7. Where would you go to see a tractor and a silo?

8. Where would you go for mail if you lived on a farm?

To You Who Teach

You, the teacher, helped to make BILLY'S NEIGHBORS. It was with you and your pupils ever in mind that the book was written and designed.

Miss Dale, the teacher in our book, typifies you who are devoted to the teaching of young children. She is warm and friendly, likes children, and enjoys teaching them. She encourages initiative, an inquiring mind, cooperation, and is always ready to give help when it is needed. She is interested in all aspects of the children's environment and tries to help them understand it and appreciate it.

The different types of children that you teach are represented in the stories. Billy is friendly and talkative. Ann is very active and self-assured. Alice is shy. Bob has a good background of information and so on.

The stories deal with situations in the children's school and their community. They present typical experiences of children, information of value, and desirable standards of conduct. They are part of a program that is based on children's interests and that will help them to become adjusted in their own worlds.

This book is one of a series and lays the foundation for understandings that will be developed at various levels. Such a planned program insures continuity, elimination of undesirable duplication, and emphasizes important learnings.

Among the distinctive features that characterize the book is a picture dictionary at the beginning of each unit. It should be useful in helping to introduce vocabulary and develop concepts. The children should continue to use it to identify words and for reference when writing exercises and simple stories.

Stories written in dialogue form will help children to identify themselves with the characters. They will also encourage review of materials without loss of interest when children read the parts of different characters each time.

The songs and poems represent an integral part of each unit. In many cases they add information, and they help to increase interest and pleasure.

The section beginning on page 150 was designed for review and for the checking of concepts. Each child should be encouraged to react to each of the exercises. This will help children to think in an orderly way and it will provide another opportunity for you to judge the effectiveness of your work.

One of your major concerns is to encourage the children in democratic living. That has been one of our major concerns in the writing of the materials. We all want to see the children grow as individuals and as members of a group. The materials were written with these objectives in mind.

The materials were drawn from many fields. They not only picture the children's environment, but they encourage full happy lives, safe living, healthy living, conservation, and consumer intelligence. Very elementary ideas of economics are presented.

Application to the children's own community should be made constantly. Children's questions should be invited, and reports of their own related experiences should be encouraged.

A *Teacher's Guide* provides specific suggestions for teaching and for realizing the objectives of primary social studies. It suggests additional activities and lists supplementary materials.

Finally, to the many teachers and children who have contributed ideas and constructive criticisms, we express our sincere thanks. We hope you will find in this book the help for which you have been looking and that its use will enhance your teaching in all fields.

We also wish to thank the post office employees and the police and fire departments in Berwyn, Illinois, the police and fire departments in St. Petersburg, Florida, for providing valuable information.

The Authors

Word List

The 317 new words used in BILLY'S NEIGHBORS are listed with the exception of plurals formed by adding s to a known word, possessives, and compound words formed from two known words. Included in the list are 21 words formed by adding a common suffix to a known word. Words presented in the dictionaries are listed for the pages where they occur first in the text.

5

6

7 Dale
   like(d)

8 grandmother's
   milk

9 beach

10 librarian
   park

11

12 draw
   their

13

14

15

16 airplane
   poem

17

18 fires
   many
   Maplewood

19 firemen

20

21 cat

engine
kinds
ladder
tree

22 again
   birds
   could

23

24 buildings
   know
   long

25 hoses
   hydrant
   sometimes
   where

26 pipe

27

28 burn
   can't
   so

29 matches
   near
   should
   then

30 drill

if

31 night
   one
   station
   told

32 pole
   room
   sleep
   upstairs

33 boats
   here
   learn
   ways

34 ready
   rings

35 any
   carry
   were
   when

36 other
   pull
   rang
   stop(ped)

37 fast

motors
strong
with

38 rules
   safety
   signs
   some
   write

39 Halloween

40

41 get(ting)
   parade
   soon

42 cut
   everyone
   eyes

43

44 jack-o-lanterns
   posters
   see(n)

45

46 leader

47 pet
   Whoo-oo

159

106 hat
part
suits
107 check
pay
thank(ed)
108 bank
next
older
109
110
111 corn
got
storekeeper
sugar
traded
112 chart
113
114
115 letter
116 Boots
117 mail
walk
118 Christmas

holidays
hours
miles
post office
119 bite
writ(ing)
120 Bill
brother
moved
moving
121
122
123 places
124
125
126 early
dairy
drink
127 garbage
yard
128 clean(ers)
snow
129 means
most
tax

tax(es)
working
130
131
132
133 barns
134 glass
135 silos
stall
136 Brownie
calf
dried
grass
hay
137 cannery
ears
plants
sweet
that's
138 machines
oats
plow
tractor
139

140 fold
141 mice
puppies
white
142 freezer
hogs
noise
pigs
until
143 chicks
hens
144 bread
sit(ting)
145 afraid
feet
I'm
swim
146 line
147 lunch
148 farm(ing)
149
150
151
152 favorite